250 Jazz & Blues All-Time Hits.

Exclusive Distributors:
Music Sales Limited
8/9 Frith Street,
London W1V 5TZ, England.
Music Sales Pty Limited
120 Rothschild Avenue,
Rosebery, NSW 2018,
Australia.

This book © Copyright 1991 by Wise Publications
Order No. AM84526
ISBN 0-7119-2624-7

Compiled by Peter Evans & Peter Lavender
Design by Pearce Marchbank Studio
Album covers courtesy of Phil Levene

Music Sales' complete catalogue lists thousands of titles and is
free from your local music shop, or direct from Music Sales Limited.
Please send a cheque/postal order for £1.50 for postage to:
Music Sales Limited, Newmarket Road, Bury St. Edmunds, Suffolk IP33 3YB.

Printed in the United Kingdom by
Scotprint Limited, Musselburgh, Edinburgh.

250 Jazz & Blues All-Time Hits.

Wise Publications
London/New York/Sydney

1. Ain't Misbehavin'

Words by Andy Razaf. Music by Thomas Waller & Harry Brooks.

Moderately

2. Angel Eyes

Words by Earl Brent. Music by Matt Dennis.

Moderately

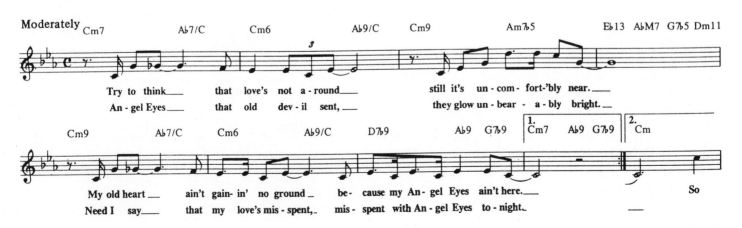

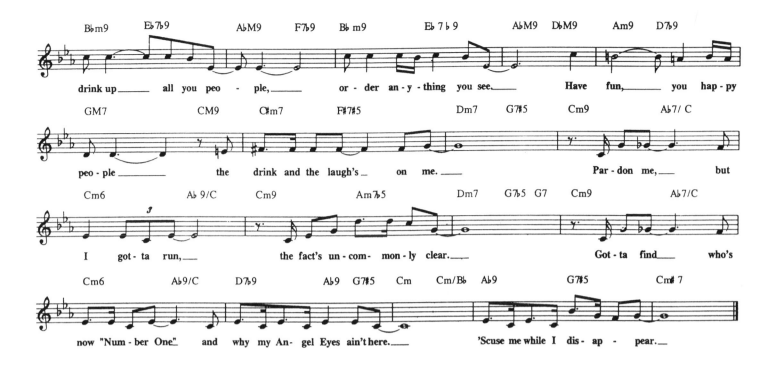

drink up_____ all you peo - ple,_____ or - der an - y - thing you see._ Have fun,_ you hap - py

peo - ple _____ the drink and the laugh's_ on me._ Par - don me,_ but

I got - ta run,_ the fact's un - com - mon - ly clear._ Got - ta find_ who's

now "Num - ber One"_ and why my An - gel Eyes ain't here._ 'Scuse me while I dis - ap - pear._

3. Albert Carroll's Blues

By Ferdinand 'Jelly Roll' Morton.

4. A Night In Tunisia

Music by Frank Paparelli & John 'Dizzy' Gillespie. Words by Raymond Leveen.

5. Airegin

By Sonny Rollins.

6. A Breeze From Alabama

By Scott Joplin.

7. Bweebida Bobbida

By Gerry Mulligan.

8. Alright, Okay, You Win

Words & Music by Sid Wyche & Mayme Watts.

9. Big Noise From Winnetka

Words by Gil Rodin & Bob Crosby. Music by Bob Haggart & Ray Baudac.

I'm called the Big Noise From Win - net - ka; and I
I just blew in from Win - net - ka, where I

play ro - man - tic parts.
broke a mil - lion hearts. Now I've had

my fun and yet, there's just one who got me from the start.

Ex - it Big Noise from Win - net - ka,

en - ter Big Noise in your heart.

10. Butler's Blues

By Yusef Lateef.

Slow blues

11. Blues Around My Bed

Words & Music by Spencer Williams.

© Copyright 1943 for all Countries by Campbell Connelly & Company Limited, 8/9 Frith Street, London W1.
All Rights Reserved. International Copyright Secured.

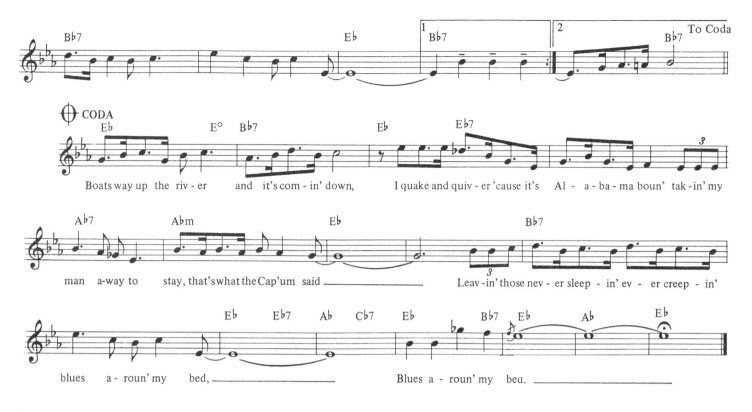

Boats way up the riv-er and it's com-in' down, I quake and quiv-er 'cause it's Al - a - ba - ma boun' tak-in' my

man a-way to stay, that's what the Cap'um said _____ Leav-in' those nev - er sleep - in' ev - er creep - in'

blues a - roun' my bed, _____ Blues a - roun' my bed. _____

12. Buddy Bolden's Blues

By Ferdinand 'Jelly Roll' Morton.
© Copyright 1992 Dorsey Brothers Music Limited, 8/9 Frith Street, London W1V 5TZ.
All Rights Reserved. International Copyright Secured.

Moderately

Thought I heard Bud-dy Bol-den say:___ "You're nas-ty, you're dir-ty, take it a-way.___ You're

ter - ri-ble___ you're aw-ful, take it a-way.___ I thought I heard him say.___ I

thought I heard___ Bud-dy Bol-den shout:___ "O-pen up that win-dow, and let that bad air out;___

O-pen up that win-dow, and let that bad air out." I thought I heard Bud-dy Bol - den shout. I

thought I heard Judge Fog-ar-ty say:___ "Thir-ty days___ in the mar-ket, take him a-way.___ Get him a

good broom to sweep with, take him a-way." I thought I heard him say:___ I

thought I heard___ Frank - ie Du-sen shout:___ 'Gal, gim-me that mon-ey, I'm gon-na beat it out.___ I mean

gim - me that mon-ey, I'm gon-na beat it out.___ 'Cause I thought I heard Frank-ie Du-sen shout.

13. Baby Won't You Please Come Home

Words & Music by Charles Warfield & Clarence Williams.

14. Bluesette

Words by Norman Gimbel. Music by Jean Thielemans.

Doo - ya, doo - ya, doo - ya, doo - ya, doo - ya, doo - ya,

Doo - oo - oo Blues - ette. _____ Pret - ty lit - tle Blues - ette must - n't be a

mourn - er. Have you heard the news yet? Love is 'round the cor - ner. Love wrapped in rain - bows and tied with pink

rib - bon to make your next spring - time your gold wed - ding ring time. So, dry your eyes. Don't - cha

pout, don't - cha fret, good - y good times are com - ing, Blues - ette. _____ Long as there's love in your

heart to share, dear blues - ette, don't des - pair. Some blue boy is long - ing, just like you, to

find a some - one to be true to. One luck - y day love - ly love will come your way. _____

____ That mag - ic day _____ may just be to - day. _____

15. Blue Haze

By Miles Davis.

© *Copyright 1965 Prestige Music Company Incorporated, USA.*
Prestige Music Limited, 1 Wyndham Yard, Wyndham Place, London W1.
All Rights Reserved. International Copyright Secured.

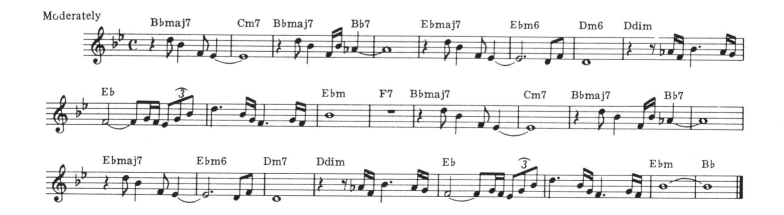

16. Beat Me Daddy, Eight To The Bar

Words & Music Don Raye, Hughie Prince & Eleanore Sheehy.

17. Blue Brew

By Memphis Slim.

18. Buddy Bertrand's Blues

By Ferdinand 'Jelly Roll' Morton.

Moderately

19. Bill Bailey Won't You Please Come Home

Traditional.

Moderately

Won't you come home, Bill Bai - ley, Won't You Come Home? She moans the whole day long; ____

____ I'll do de cook - ing, dar - ling I'll pay de rent, I know I've done you

wrong. _____ 'Mem - ber dat rain - y eve dat I drove you out, wid noth - in but a

fine tooth comb? ____ I know I'se to blame, well, ain't dat a shame? Bill

Bai - ley, Won't You Please Come Home? ____ Home? ____

Bird Feathers

By Charlie Parker.

21. Be-Bop

By John 'Dizzy' Gillespie.

22. Blue Blood Blues

By Ferdinand 'Jelly Roll' Morton.

23. Bluing

By Miles Davis.

24. Blue 'N' Boogie

By John 'Dizzy' Gillespie & Frank Paparelli.

Moderately fast

25. Boogie Woogie Bugle Boy

Words & Music by Don Raye & Hughie Prince.

Moderately

bass and gui - tar ___ is play-in' with 'im. ___ He makes the comp -'ny jump when he plays re - veil - le He's the Boo-gie Woo-gie Bu-gle Boy of Com-pa-ny B! ___ He Com-pa - ny B! ___

26. Bags' Groove

By Milt Jackson.

© Copyright 1958 Wemar Music Corporation, USA.
Rights administered by George Wiener Music Limited, London.
All Rights Reserved. International Copyright Secured.

Moderately

27. Come Sunday

By Duke Ellington.

© Copyright 1966 Tempo Music Incorporated, USA.
Campbell Connelly & Company Limited, 8/9 Frith Street, London W1V 5TZ.
All Rights Reserved. International Copyright Secured.

Medium swing

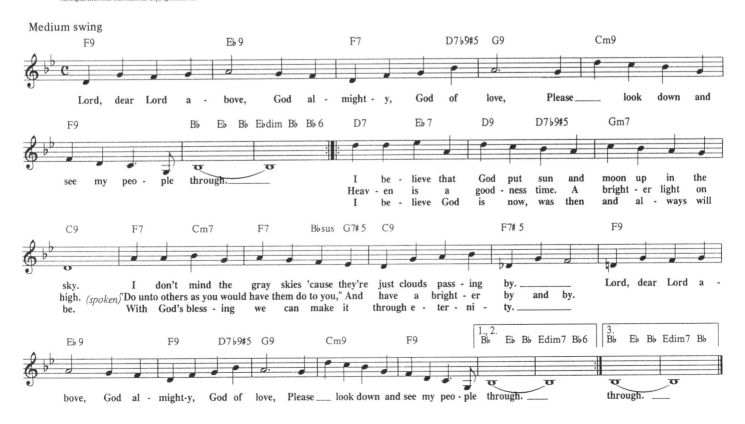

Lord, dear Lord a - bove, God al - might - y, God of love, Please ___ look down and

see my peo - ple through. ___
Heav - en is a good - ness time. A bright - er light on
I be - lieve God is now, was then and al - ways will

sky. I don't mind the gray skies 'cause they're just clouds pass - ing by. ___ Lord, dear Lord a -
high. (spoken) "Do unto others as you would have them do to you," And have a bright - er by and by.
be. With God's bless - ing we can make it through e - ter - ni - ty. ___

bove, God al - might-y, God of love, Please ___ look down and see my peo - ple through. ___ through.

28. Canal Street Blues

By Joe 'King' Oliver.
© Copyright 1923 Joseph Oliver, USA.
© Copyright 1949 International Music Incorporated, USA.
Campbell Connelly & Company Limited, 8/9 Frith Street, London W1.
All Rights Reserved. International Copyright Secured.

29. Cry! Tender – 1

By Yusef Lateef.
© Copyright 1972 Prestige Music Company Incorporated, USA.
Prestige Music Limited, 1 Wyndham Yard, Wyndham Place, London W1.
All Rights Reserved. International Copyright Secured.

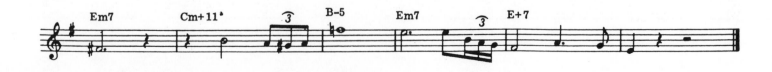

30. Cry! Tender – 2

By Yusef Lateef.

31. Cute

Words by Stanley Styne. Music by Neal Hefti.

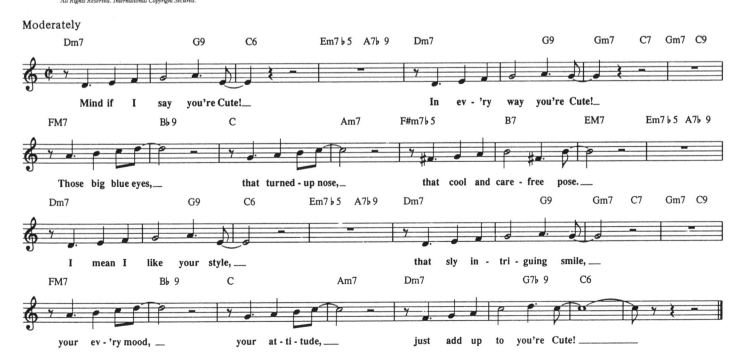

32. Cinnamon And Clove

Music by Johnny Mandel. Words by Marilyn Bergman & Alan Bergman.

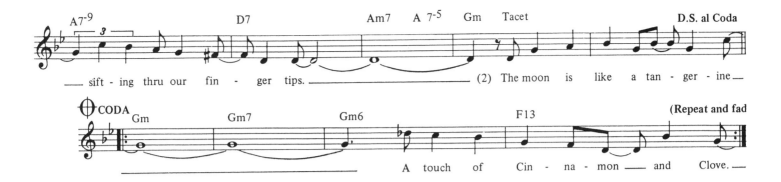

33. Chega De Saudade (No More Blues)

Original Words by Vinicius de Moraes. English Words by Jon Hendricks &
Jessie Cavanaugh. Music by Antonio C. Jobim.

34. Caravan

By Duke Ellington, Irving Mills & Juan Tizol.

35. Chattanoogie Shoe Shine Boy

Words & Music by Henry Stone & Jack Strapp.

feel as tho' you want to dance when he gets thro'__ He's a great big bun-dle of joy__

He pops a boog-ie woog-ie rag The Chat-ta-noog-ie Shoe Shine Boy __

It's a won-der that the rag don't tear the way he makes it pop__ You

ought to see him fan the air __ with his hop-pi-ty hip-pi-ty hip-pi-pi hop-pi-ty

hop-pi-ty hip-pi-ty hop He o-pens up for bus-'ness when the clock strike's nine __ He

likes to get 'em ear-ly when they're feel-in' fine__ Ev-'ry-bo-dy gets a lit-tle

rise__ and shine__ with the great big bun-dle of joy____ He pops a boog-ie woog-ie rag The

Chat-ta-noog-ie Shoe shine Boy. ____ Have you

36. The Champ

By John 'Dizzy' Gillespie.

© Copyright 1953 Editions Musicales Vogue Records.
Peter Maurice Music Company Limited, 127 Charing Cross Road, London WC2.
All Rights Reserved. International Copyright Secured.

Fast bop

37. Cantiga Nova Swing

By Dave Brubeck.

38. Chicago Breakdown

By Ferdinand 'Jelly Roll' Morton.

39. Dig

By Miles Davis.

40. Chelsea Bridge

By Billy Strayhorn.

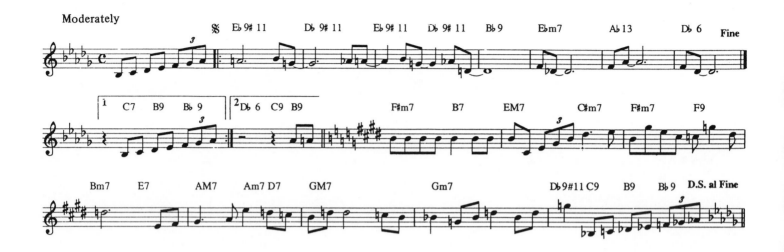

41. Dizzy Atmosphere

By John 'Dizzy' Gillespie.

42. Do You Have Soul Now

By King Curtis.

43. Don't Argue

By Kai Winding.

44. Desafinado (Slightly Out Of Tune)

English Lyric by Jon Hendricks & Jessie Cavanaugh.
Music by Antonio Carlos Jobim.

Bossa nova

sing a song of lov - ing, We're bound to get in tune a - gain be - fore too

long. There'll be no De - sa - fi - na - do when your heart be - longs to me com - plete - ly.

___ Then you won't be Slight - ly Out Of Tune,___ You'll sing a - long with me.___

45. Down

By Miles Davis.

46. Down The Line

By Gene Ammons.

47. Dexterious

Moderately

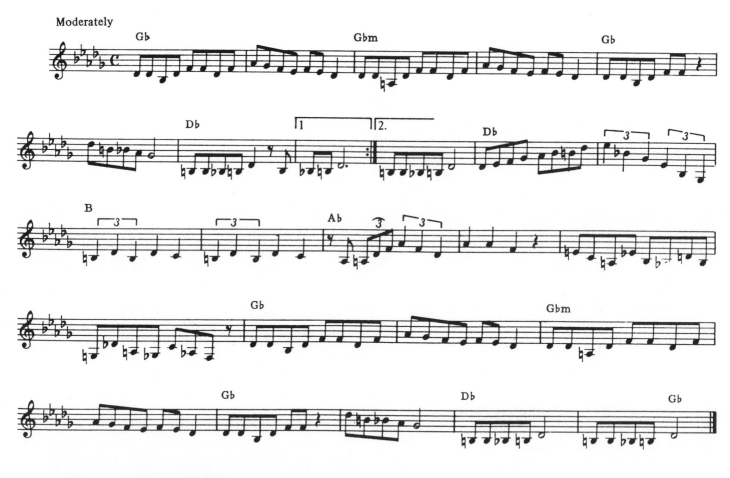

48. Drop Me Off In Harlem

Moderately

Drop me off ___ in Har - lem, ___ An - y place ___ in Har - lem, ___ There's some - one wait - ing there who makes it seem like hea - ven up in Har - lem, ___ I don't want ___ your Dix - ie, ___

You can keep— your Dix - ie, — There's no - one down in Dix - ie who can take me
'way from my own Har - lem, — Har - lem has — those south-ern skies, — They're in my ba - by's smile.
— I i - dol - ize — my ba - by's eyes — and class - y up - town style. If
Har - lem moved — to Chi - na, — I know of no - thing fi - ner, — Than to
stow a - way — on a 'plane some day and have them drop me off in Har - lem. — Har - lem.

49. Don't Stand Up

By Oliver Nelson.

Fast

50. Denial

By Miles Davis.

Moderately

51. The Duke

Music by Dave Brubeck. Words by Iola Brubeck.

Moderately

We miss you, Duke.___ We miss you so.___ We miss your smile that set our
You wailed, ba - by,___ you wailed a storm.___ Af - ter he made you, God just

hearts a - glow.___ We miss your suave and gra - cious ways.___ We loved you mad - ly
broke the form. ___ You are a man be - yond com - pare,___ So af - ter you all

all your days.___ You had such a lyr - ic line___ and a style words
men seen square.___ When you sent us we stayed gone___ Peo - ple asked us

can't de - fine.___ your soul - ful phras - es did a - maze us more than Wil - liam
(Spoken)"What you on?"___ to quote a phrase from ol' Satch- mo___ "If you got to ask you'll

Shake-speare's plays___ We dig, ba - by,___ we dig you so___
nev - er know___ we were on love You swing, ba - by,___ you swing for me___

we're gon - na miss you more than you could know.___ Your love and mu-sic, a mel - low mix___
we vote you jazz-man of the cen - tu - ry_____ We'll al - ways sing your mel - o -dies___

It's all we need - ed for some kicks. Sing-in', swing-in' no life's com -plete___ un -
and swing to your sweet har - mo - nies.

til he's known the rhy - thm of that El - ling -ton beat.___ Liv - in', lov - in' the

hu - man race,___ he made this cra - zy mixed -up world a {swing - in'} place.___
{lov - in'}

52. Don't Mind If I Do

By Buddy Tate.

Moderately

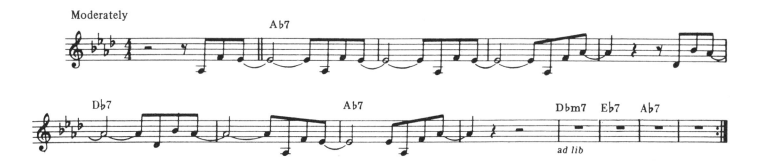

ad lib

53. Django

By John Lewis.

Slow

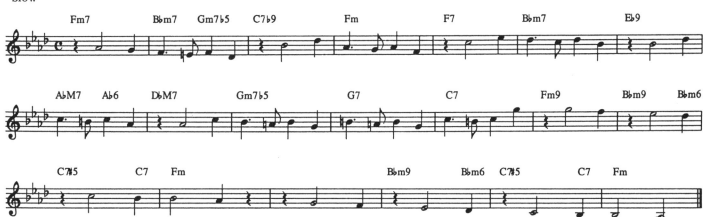

54. Doxy

By Sonny Rollins.

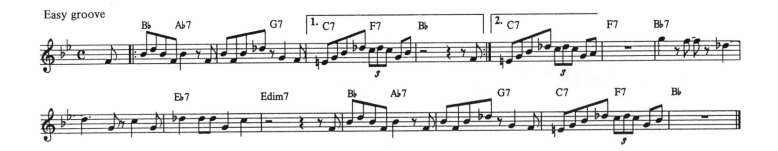

55. Emanon

By 'Dizzy' Gillespie & Milt Shaw.

56. The Entertainer

By Scott Joplin.

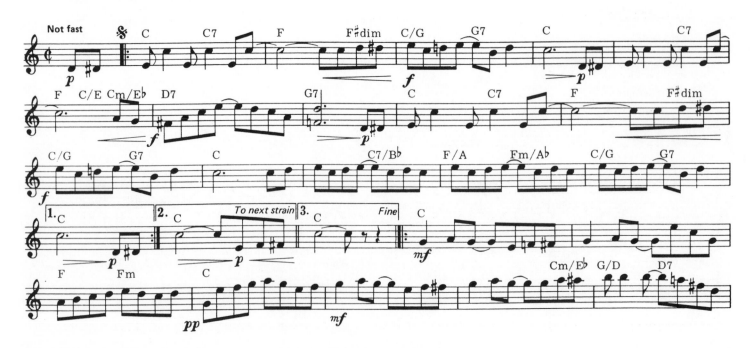

57. Early Autumn

Words by Johnny Mercer. Music by Ralph Burns & Woody Herman.

58. Freight Trane

By Tommy Flanagan.

59. Epilogue

By Bill Evans.

(Melody from ⊕ played in 4th's or 5th's or 6th's within E♭ scale.
Bass plays 5th's on tones indicated throughout.)

60. The Funky Fox

By Shirley Scott.

Uptempo swing

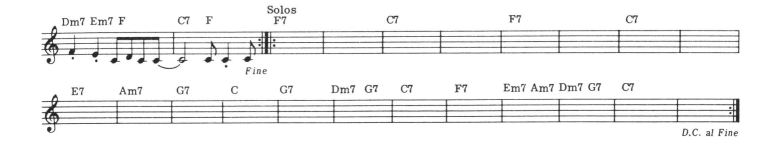

61. Four

By Miles Davis.

62. Four Brothers

By Jimmy Giuffre.

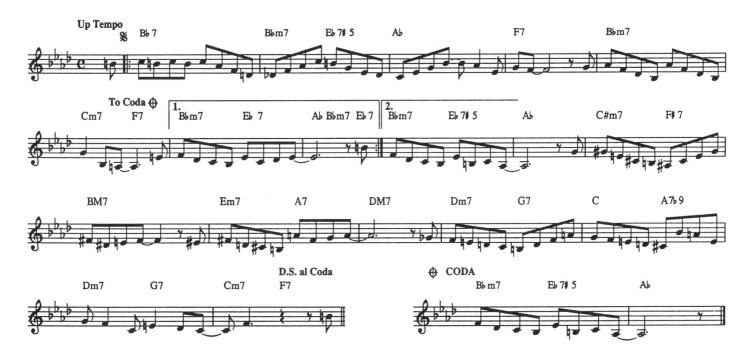

63. Flying Home

By Benny Goodman & Lionel Hampton.

64. For Lena And Lenny

By Quincy Jones.

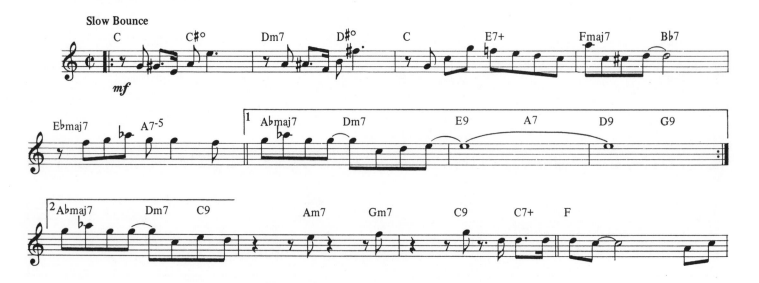

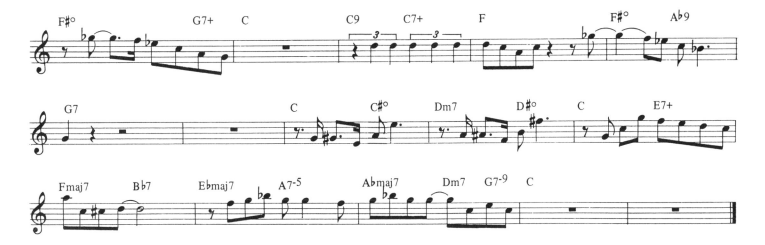

65. Good Bait

By Tadd Dameron & Count Basie.

66. Gambling Jack

By Ferdinand 'Jelly Roll' Morton.

67. Go Away Blues

Words & Music by Duke Ellington.

68. Groovin' High

By John 'Dizzy' Gillespie.

69. Hawk Eyes

By Coleman Hawkins.

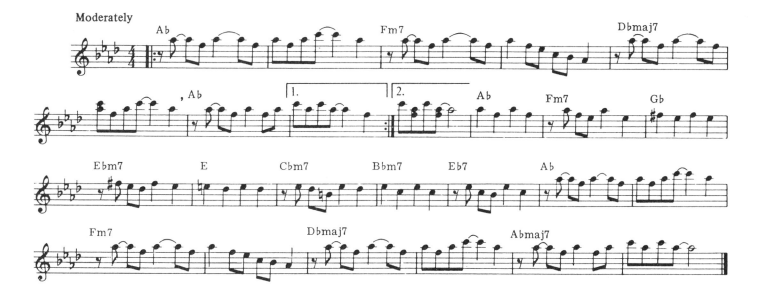

70. The Hawk Talks

By Louis Bellson.
© Copyright 1954 Tempo Music Incorporated, USA.
Campbell Connelly & Company Limited, 8/9 Frith Street, London W1.
All Rights Reserved. International Copyright Secured.

71. Hey! Ba-Ba-Re-Bop

Words & Music by Lionel Hampton & Curley Hammer.
© Copyright 1945, 1946 MCA Music (a division of MCA Incorporated, USA).
MCA Music Limited, 77 Fulham Palace Road, London W6 for the World (excluding North, Central and South America,
Australasia, Japan and the Philippines).
All Rights Reserved. International Copyright Secured.

72. Honeysuckle Rose

Music by Thomas 'Fats' Waller. Words by Andy Razaf.

Moderately

73. How Insensitive

Music by Antonio Carlos Jobim. Original Lyrics by Vinicius De Moraes.
English Lyrics by Norman Gimbel.

74. Hip Soul

By Stanley Turrentine.

75. History Of A Boy Scout

By Dave Brubeck.

76. Hot Dog

By Zoot Sims.

77. Hong Pong

By Shirley Scott.

78. I Know

By Miles Davis.

79. Hip Twist

By Stanley Turrentine.

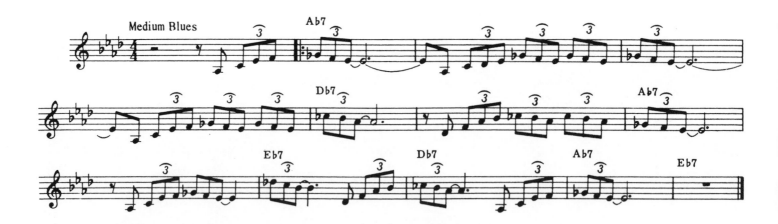

80. Is You Is, Or Is You Ain't (Ma' Baby)

Words & Music by Billy Austin & Louis Jordan.

Is You Is, Or Is You Ain't ma' ba- by? May - be ba - by's found some- bod - y new; _____ or

is ma' ba - by still ma' ba - by true? _ still ma' ba - by true? _____

81. I Wish I Knew How It Would Feel To Be Free

Words by Billy Taylor & Dick Dallas. Music by Billy Taylor.

Moderately

1 & 5 I wish I knew how it would feel to be free. _
2 wish I could share _____ all the love _____ in my heart _
3 wish I could give _____ all I'm long - ing to give _
4 wish I could be _____ like a bird _____ in the sky _

_____ I wish I could break _____ all these chains _____ hold - ing me. _
re - move all the bars _____ that still keep _____ us a - part. _
I wish I could live _____ like I'm long - ing to live. _
how sweet it would be _____ if I found _____ I could fly. _

_____ I wish I could say _____ all the things _
I wish you could know _____ what it means _
I wish I could do _____ all the things _
I'd soar to the sun _____ and look down _

_____ I should say, _____ Say 'em loud, _____ Say 'em clear, _
to be me, _____ Then you'd see _____ and a - gree _
I can do, _____ Though I'm way _____ ov - er - due _
at the sea, _____ Then I'd sing _____ 'cause I'd know _

_____ for the whole _____ world to hear. _____ I
ev - 'ry man _____ should be free. _____ I
I'd be start - ing a - new. _____ I
how it feels _____ to be free. _____ Last time Fine

82. Into It

By Stan Getz.

Moderately

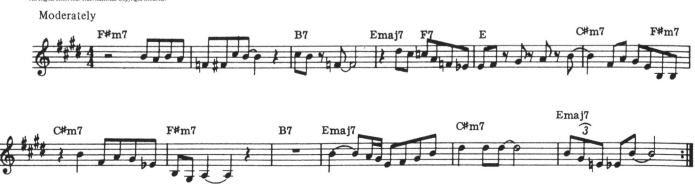

83. Intermission Riff

Words by Steve Graham. Music by Ray Wetzel.

It's be - gin - ning, / Trum - pets driv - in' / In - ter - mis - sion Riff. / Real - ly spin - ning, / Come a - live in

In - ter - mis - sion Riff. / Keep__ that or - gan go - ing__ and keep that mu - sic flow- in'. / High - er, go - ing high - er,__ those horns will catch on fire.__

Hear that beat of / Sax - es rid - din' / In - ter - mis - sion Riff. / Feel that heat of / Trom - bones slid - in'

In - ter - mis - sion Riff. / Cool__ and oh, so groo - vy,__ gee, how this tune can move me. / Take__ an - oth - er cho - rus,__ it's nev - er too much for us.

84. It's A Raggy Waltz

By Dave Brubeck.

85. I'm Beginning To See The Light

Words & Music by Harry James, Duke Ellington, Johnny Hodges & Don George.

Moderately

I   nev - er cared much   for moon-lit   skies,   I   nev - er wink back   at   fi - re   flies,   but
nev - er went   in   for af - ter   glow,   or   can - dle light on   the mist - le - toe,   but
nev - er made love   by lan-tern   shine,   I   nev - er saw rain-bows in   my   wine,   but

now that the stars   are   in your   eyes,
now when you turn   the lamp down low   }   I'm Be - gin - ning To See The   Light.
now that your lips   are   burn-ing mine,

I

Used   to ram - ble thru the   park,   shad - ow box - ing in the dark,   then you came and

caused a   spark,   that's a   four al - arm   fi - re   now.___   I

D.S. 𝄋 al FINE
(without repeat)

In A Sentimental Mood

Words & Music by Duke Ellington, Irving Mills & Manny Kurtz.

In A Sen-ti-men-tal Mood _____ I can see the stars come thru my room _____ While your lov-ing at-ti-tude _____ is like a flame that lights the gloom, On the wings of ev-'ry kiss _____ Drifts a mel-o-dy so strange and sweet _____ In this sen-ti-men-tal bliss _____ you make my Par - a - dise com - plete. Rose pet-als seem to fall It's all like a dream to call you mine, My heart's a light-er thing since you made this night a thing di - vine, In A Sen-ti-men-tal Mood _____ I'm with-in a world so hea-ven-ly _____ For I ne-ver dreamt that you'd _____ be lov-ing sen - ti - men - tal me.

87. I Mean You

By Thelonious Monk & Coleman Hawkins.

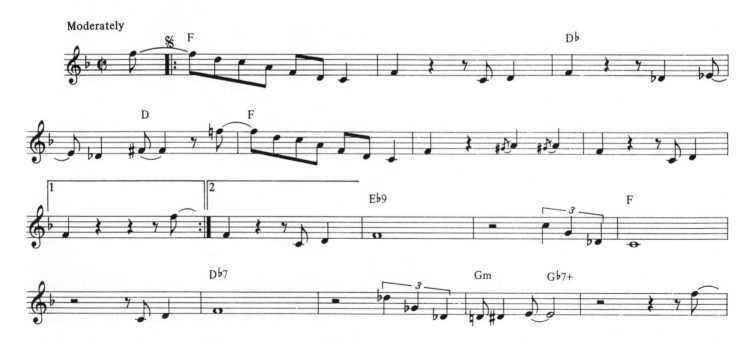

88. I Remember Clifford

By Benny Golson.

89. In Your Own Sweet Way

Music by Dave Brubeck. Words by Iola Brubeck.

In your own sweet way you've turned the whole world up - side down,__
plain to see. I'm noth - ing but a pass - ing phase.__

Put on the false face, played the clown.__ Well, you've had your say. Now, it's
You don't in - tend to mend your ways__ to re -

main with me. I found your style A - mus - ing

for a while_____ I watched you have your fun with ev - 'ry - one in your

own sweet way. I know your terms. I know them well.__ I'm turn - ing flip-flops,

I can tell that you'd like to stay your own sweet way._____

90. I'll Remember April

Words & Music by Don Raye, Gene de Paul & Patricia Johnson.

This love - ly day will leng -then in - to ev - 'ning, we'll sigh good - bye to all we've ev - er had.____ A -
The fire will dwin - dle in - to glow - ing ash - es, for flames and love live such a lit - tle while. __ I

lone, where we have walked to - geth - er, _____ I'll Re - mem - ber A - pril ___ and be glad. _____ I'll

be con - tent ____ you loved me once in A - pril. your lips were warm_ and love and Spring were new.__ But I'm not a -

fraid of Au - tumn and her sor - row, ____ for I'll Re - mem - ber ____ A - pril and you. ____

CODA

won't for-get, ____ but I won't be lone-ly, ____ I'll Re-mem-ber A-pril, ___ and I'll smile. ____

91. Infant Eyes

By Wayne Shorter.

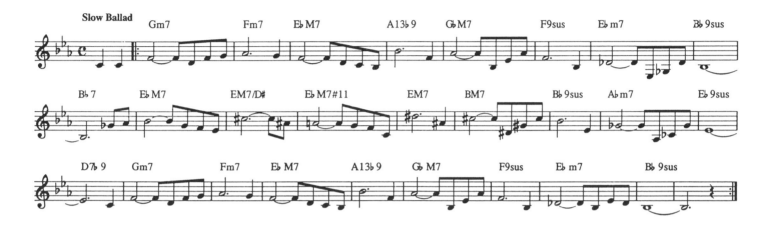

Slow Ballad

92. Jammin' With Gene

By Gene Ammons.

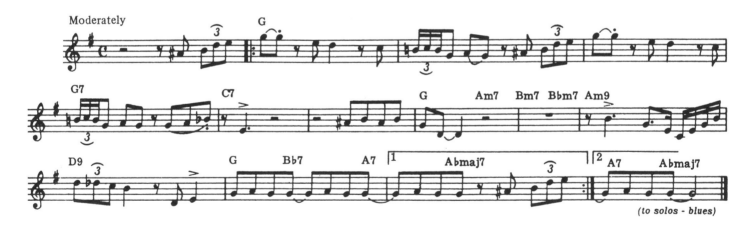

Moderately

(to solos - blues)

93. Jams And Jellies

By Oliver Nelson.

Moderately

solo break

(for solos, play regular blues)

94. Inner Space

By Chick Corea.

95. Jelly Roll Blues

By Ferdinand 'Jelly Roll' Morton.

96. Jordu

By Duke Jordan.

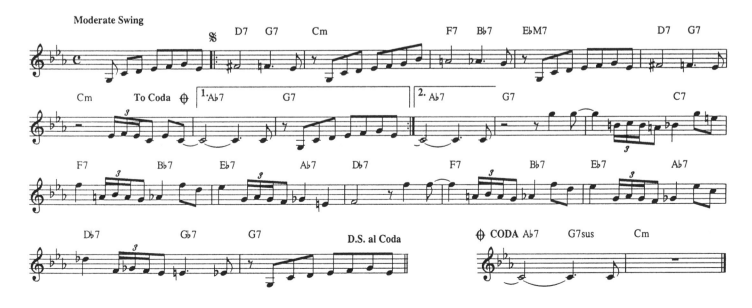

97. The Joint Is Jumpin'

Words by Andy Razaf & J.C. Johnson. Music by Thomas Waller.

98. J.D.'s Boogie Woogie

By Jimmy Dorsey & Marvin Wright.

99. Jug Eyes

By Gene Ammons.

Moderately

100. Jane-O

By Zoot Sims.

101. Kansas City Stomp

By Ferdinand 'Jelly Roll' Morton.

102. Kaper

By Gerry Mulligan.

Moderately

103. Key Club Cookout

By Charles Earland.

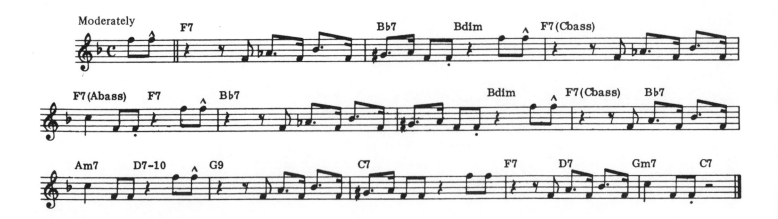

104. Lush Life

Words & Music by Billy Strayhorn.

life is aw - ful a - gain, a trough - ful of hearts could on - ly be a bore. A

week in Pa - ris will ease the bite of it; all I care is to smile in spite of it.

I'll for - get you I will while yet you are still burn - ing in - side my brain. Ro -

mance is mush, sti - fling those who strive.__ I'll live a Lush Life in some small dive,__ and

there I'll be, while I rot with the rest of those whose lives are lone - ly too.

105. Li'l Darlin'

By Neal Hefti.

106. Line For Lyons

By Gerry Mulligan.

107. Let's Dance

Words & Music by Fanny Baldridge, Gregory Stone & Joseph Bonime.

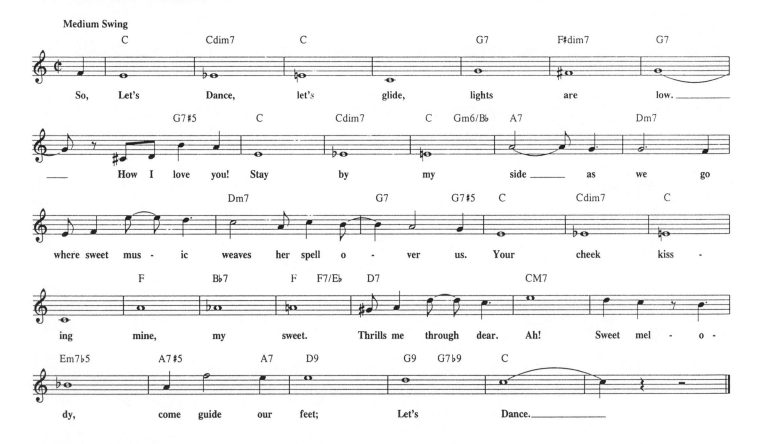

108. Lean Baby

Words by Roy Alfred. Music by Billy May.

Moderately

My Lean Ba-by tall and thin, five foot sev-en of bones and shin, but when she
She's so skin-ny, she's so drawn, when she stands side-ways you think she's gone, but when she
My Lean Ba-by, she's so slim, a broom-stick's wid-er but not as trim, and when she

tells me may-be she loves me, I feel as mel-low as a fel-low can be.
calls me ba-by I feel fine, to think she's fran-tic-'lly ro-man-tic-'lly mine.
starts to kiss me then I know I love her, so I'll nev-er ev-er let her go.

she's slen-der, but she's ten-der, she makes my heart sur-ren-der, and

ev-'ry night when I hold her tight the feel-ing is nice, my arms can go a-round twice.

109. Lover Man (Oh Where Can You Be)

Words & Music by Jimmy Davies, Roger Ram Ramirez & Jimmy Sherman.

Moderately

I don't know why, but I'm feel-ing so sad, I long to try some-thing
The night is cold, and I'm so all a-lone, I'd give my soul just to
Some day we'll meet and you'll dry all my tears, Then whis-per sweet lit-tle

I've nev-er had, nev-er had no kiss-in' oh, what I've been miss-in',
call you my own, got a moon a-bove me, but no one to love me,
things in my ears, hug-gin' and a-kiss-in', oh, what we've been miss-in',

Lov-er Man, oh where can you be?
Lov-er Man, oh where can you be? I've heard it said that the
Lov-er Man, oh where can you

thrill of ro-mance can be like a heav-en-ly dream, I go to bed with a

pray'r that you'll make love to me, strange as it seems.

be?

110. Little Brother's Soul

By King Curtis.

111. Lemon Drop

By George Wallington.

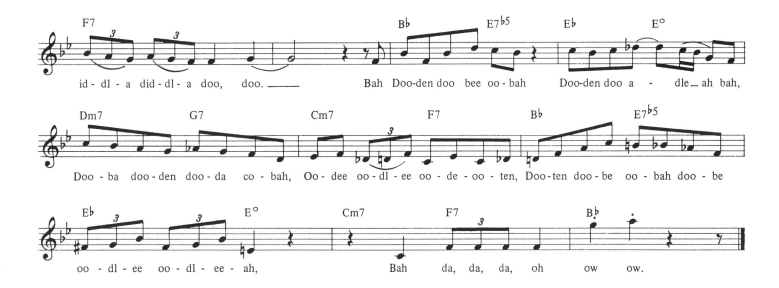

id-dl-a did-dl-a doo, doo. ___ Bah Doo-den doo bee oo-bah Doo-den doo a - dle_ah bah,

Doo - ba doo-den doo-da co-bah, Oo - dee oo-dl-ee oo-de-oo-ten, Doo-ten doo-be oo-bah doo-be

oo-dl-ee oo-dl-ee-ah, Bah da, da, da, oh ow ow.

112. Lazy Soul

By King Curtis.

113. Living Soul

By Richard 'Groove' Holmes.

114. Lullaby Of Birdland

Music by George Shearing. Words by George David Weiss.

Lul - la - by Of Bird-land that's what I ____ al - ways hear ____ when you sigh. ____

Nev - er in my word-land could there be ways ____ to re - veal ____ in a phrase ____ how I feel! ____

Have you ev - er heard two tur - tle doves ____ bill and coo ____ when they love? ____

That's the kind of mag - ic mu - sic we make ____ with our lips ____ when we kiss! ____

And there's a weep - y old wil - low; ____ he real - ly knows how to cry! ____

That's how I'd cry in my pil - low ____ if you should tell me fare - well ____ and good - bye!

Lul - la - by Of Bird - land whis - per low, ____ kiss me sweet ____ and we'll go ____

fly - in' high in bird - land, high in the sky ____ up a - bove ____ all be - cause

____ we're in love! ____ all be - cause ____ we're in love.

115. Mambo Bounde

By Sonny Rollins.

116. Lonesome (Si Tu Vois Ma Mère)

By Sidney Bechet.

117. Minor Mood – 1

By Yusef Lateef.

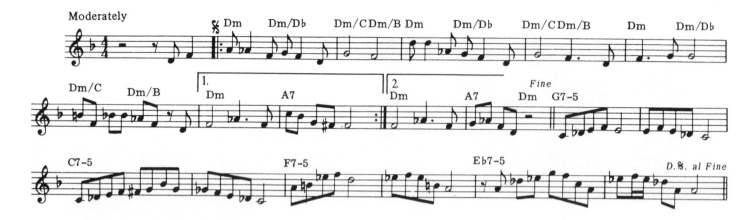

118. Minor Mood – 2

By Yusef Lateef.

119. Manteca

Words & Music by 'Dizzy' Gillespie & Gil Fuller.

editation (Meditacao)

rds by Newton Mendonca English Lyric by Norman Gimbel.
tonio Carlos Jobim.
3 Antonio Carlos Jobim and Mrs Newton Mendonca, Brazil.
7 Fulham Palace Road, London W6 for the British Commonwealth (excluding Canada) South Africa
ed. International Copyright Secured.

Bossa nova

C6   B7sus   B7   C6

In _____ my lone - li - ness _____ When you're gone ___ and I'm all ___ by my - self
Though _____ you're far ___ a - way _____ I have on - ly to close _____ my eyes
I _____ will wait _ for you _____ 'till the sun _ falls from out _ of the sky

Em7   A7# 5   Dm7   Bb 7

___ and I ___ need your ___ ca - ress. _____ I _____ just think of you _____
___ and you ___ are back ___ to stay. _____ I _____ just close _ my eyes _____
___ for what _ else can ___ I do? _____ I _____ will wait _ for you _____

To Coda ⊕   Em7   A7# 5   Dm7

_____ and the thought _ of you hold - ing me near _____ make my lon - li - ness soon _ dis - a - pear _____
_____ and the sad - ness that miss - ing you brings _____ soon is gone ___ and this heart _ of mine sings. _____
_____ Med - i - ta -

1. G7   2. G7   FM7   Bb 7   Em7   Eb dim7

___ Yes, _____ I love ___ you so _____ and that _ for me _ is all ___ I need to know _____

Dm7   D.C. al Coda   G 7   ⊕ CODA   Em7   A7# 5   Dm7   G 7b 9   C6

_____ - ting how sweet _ life will be _____ when you come _ back to me. _____

121. Mad About Him, Sad Without Him, How Can I Be Glad Without Him Blues

Words & Music by Larry Markes & Dick Charles.

© Copyright 1942 MCA Music (a division of MCA Incorporated, USA).
MCA Music Limited, 77 Fulham Palace Road, London W6 for the world (excluding North, South and Central America, Japan,
Australasia and the Philippines).
All Rights Reserved. International Copyright Secured.

Moderately

C   C7

I went to bed last eve - nin' feel - in' blue as I could be. _____ I could - n't

F7   C

sleep last eve - nin' with what was wor - ry - in' me. _____ Oh the

G7   F   G7   C

tears I've wast - ed would sure - ly fill the deep blue sea. _____ I've got those

C7

cry a - bout {him / her,} die with - out {him / her} Lor - dy where am I with- out {him / her} blues. _____ {He / She} keeps me

walk-in' on the floor / hang-in' 'round her door and like a fool I ask for more. _____ Al-tho' I know {he/she} is-n't good I would-n't leave {him/her} if I could ah no. _____ I'm not the first on {his/her} list, ___ I'd nev-er be missed, ___ I wish I had a dime for ev'-ry {gal he's/guy she's} kissed I swear _____ I'd be a mil-lion-aire. _____ And yet I would-n't care ___ as long as I could get my ___ share. _____ I've got those Mad A-bout {Him/her} Sad With-out {Him/her} How Can I Be Glad With-out {Him/her} Blues. _____ {He/She} makes my dreams go up in smoke, and then {he/she} treat it like a joke, _____ He's just an orn 'ry sort o' guy, and yet I'll

1. love him 'til I die poor me. _____
2. I went to

122. Morgan

By Charles Earland.

Moderately

123. Memphis Blues

Words & Music by W.C. Handy.

sets me wild ___ to hear that love - ly tune a - gain, those Mem-phis Blues. ___

124. Maple Leaf Rag

By Scott Joplin.

125. Midnight Sun

Words by Johnny Mercer. Music by Sonny Burke & Lionel Hampton.

126. Miles Ahead

By Miles Davis.

Moderately

127. Moanin'

Words by Jon Hendricks. Music by Bobby Timmons.

Fairly slow

Ev - 'ry morn - ing finds me moan - in', 'cause of all the trou - ble— I see, —

Life's a los - in' gam - ble— to me, — cares and woes have got me moan - in',

ev' - ry eve -nin' finds me moan-in', I'm a-lone and cry - in' — the blues. — I'm so tired of pay -

- in' these dues, — Ev' - ry bo-dy knows I'm moan - in'. — Lord I spend plen-ty of days and

nights a - lone with my grief, — And I pray real-ly and tru - ly pray some-bo - dy will come

— and bring me re - lief. Ev' - ry morn - in' finds me moan - in', 'cause of all the trou -

— bles — I see, — Life's a los - in' gam - ble— to me, — cares and woes have got me

moan - in', — Ev' - ry morn - in' finds me —

Moonglow

Words & Music by Will Hudson, Eddie de Lange & Irving Mills.

129. Moten's Swing

By Buster & Bennie Moten.

130. Mr. Jelly Lord

By Ferdinand 'Jelly Roll' Morton.

131. Mullenium

By Gerry Mulligan.

132. Mulligan's Too

By Gerry Mulligan.

133. Minor Mishap

By Tommy Flanagan

134. New Orleans Blues

By Ferdinand 'Jelly Roll' Morton.

New Orleans Bump

Ferdinand 'Jelly Roll' Morton.

136. Night Train

Words by Oscar Washington and Lewis C. Simpkins. Music by Jimmy Forrest.

Night Train that took my ba - by so far a - way, _____

Night Train that took my ba - by so far a - way, _____

Tell her I love her more and more ev - 'ry day. _____ My

moth - er said I'd lose her if I ev - er did a - buse her, should have lis - tened. _____ My

moth - er said I'd lose her if I ev - er did a - buse her, should have lis - tened. _____ Now

I have learned my les-son, my sweet ba-by was a bless-ing, should have lis-tened. _____

Night Train your whis-tle tore my poor heart in two, _____

Night Train your whis-tle tore my poor heart in two, _____

She's gone and I don't know what I'm gon-na do! _____

137. No Moe

By Sonny Rollins.

Moderately

138. Night Flight

By R. Bryant.

Moderately

Repeat & Fade

139. 9.20 Special

Words by Bill Engvick. Music by Earl Warren.

140. Now He Sings, Now He Sobs

By Chick Corea.

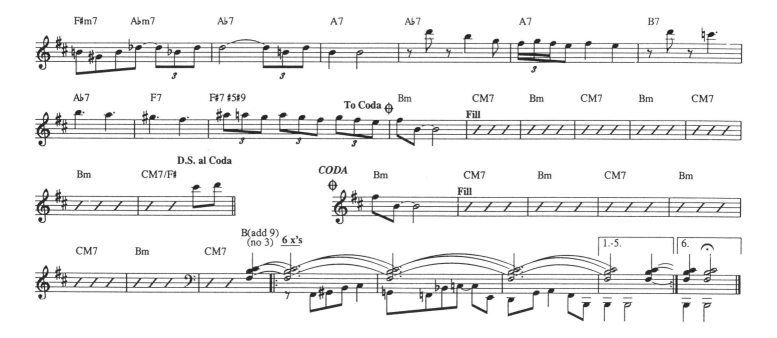

141. Night Hawk

By Coleman Hawkins.

142. Newk's Fadeaway

By Sonny Rollins.

© Copyright 1972 Prestige Music Company Incorporated, USA.
Prestige Music Limited, 1 Wyndham Yard, Wyndham Place, London W1.
All Rights Reserved. International Copyright Secured.

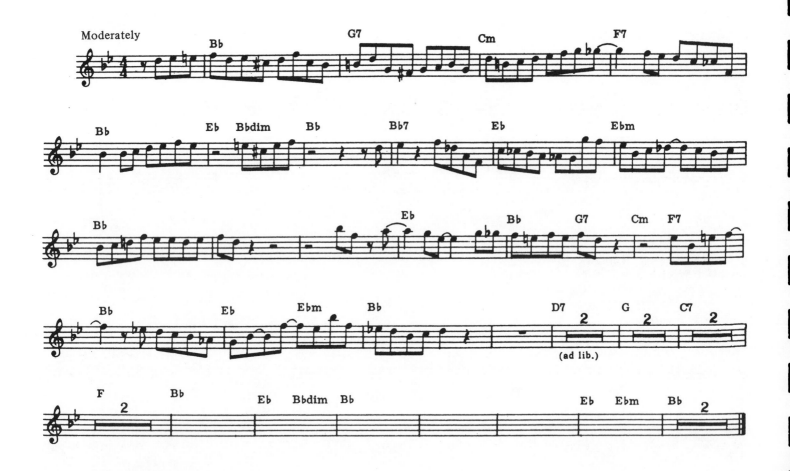

143. Ostinato

By Oliver Nelson.

© Copyright 1964 Prestige Music Company Incorporated, USA.
Prestige Music Limited, 1 Wyndham Yard, Wyndham Place, London W1.
All Rights Reserved. International Copyright Secured.

144. No Line

By Miles Davis.

145. Ornithology

By Charlie Parker & Benny Harris.

146. Out Of The Blue

By Miles Davis.

147. Opus V

By J.J. Johnson.

148. Oop Bop Sh-Bam

By John 'Dizzy' Gillespie & Walter G. Fuller.

149. Prelude To A Kiss

Words & Music by Duke Ellington, Irving Gordon & Irving Mills.

Moderately slow

150. Pent Up House

By Sonny Rollins.

151. Ol' Man Mose

By Louis Armstrong & Zilner Trenton Randolph.

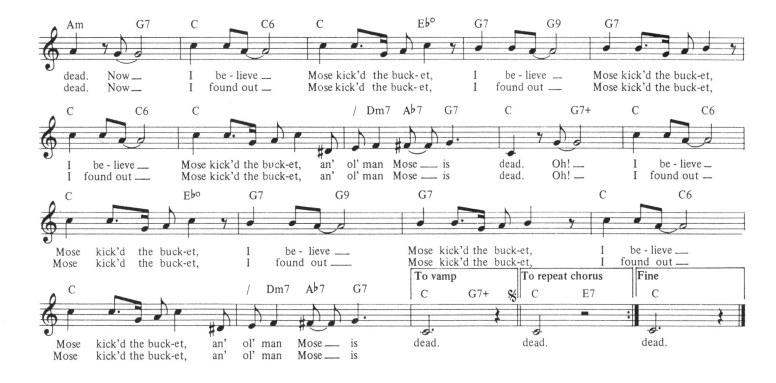

dead. Now ___ I be - lieve ___ Mose kick'd the buck-et, I be - lieve ___ Mose kick'd the buck-et,
dead. Now ___ I found out ___ Mose kick'd the buck-et, I found out ___ Mose kick'd the buck-et,

I be - lieve ___ Mose kick'd the buck-et, an' ol' man Mose ___ is dead. Oh! ___ I be - lieve ___
I found out ___ Mose kick'd the buck-et, an' ol' man Mose ___ is dead. Oh! ___ I found out ___

Mose kick'd the buck-et, I be - lieve ___ Mose kick'd the buck-et, I be - lieve ___
Mose kick'd the buck-et, I found out ___ Mose kick'd the buck-et, I found out ___

Mose kick'd the buck-et, an' ol' man Mose ___ is dead. dead. dead.
Mose kick'd the buck-et, an' ol' man Mose ___ is

152. Pompton Turnpike

Words & Music by Will Osborne & Dick Rogers.

Moderately

Pomp - ton ___ Turn - pike, ___ That's a ver - y fa - mous Jer - sey road - way ___

full of ___ coun - try ___ charm. ___ Pomp - ton ___

Turn - pike ___ leads you to a place not far from Broad - way. ___ Still it's ___ on a ___

farm. ___ You dine with lights sub - dued. ___ The mu - sic

in - ter - lude ___ puts you right in the mood ___ to dance and find your -

self ro - mance. ___ Pomp - ton ___ Turn - pike ___ ride your bike or if you like just

hitch - hike. ___ Come to ___ Pomp - ton ___ Turn - pike. ___

153. Perdido

Music by Juan Tizol. Words by Harry Lenk and Ervin Drake.

Per - di - do, __ I look for my heart, it's Per - di - do. __ I lost it way down in Tor - ri - do, __ while
le - ro, __ she glanced as she danced a bo - le - ro. I said, tak - ing off my som - bre - ro, __ "Let's

chanc - ing a dance fi - es - ta. __ Bo - es - ta." __ High was the sun when we first __
meet for a sweet si -

came close; low was the moon when we said, __ "A - dios!" Per - di - do, __ Since then has my heart been Per -

di - do, __ I know I must go to Tor - ri - do, __ that yearn - ing to lose Per - di - do. __

154. One Note Samba (Samba De Uma Nota So)

Original Words by N. Mendonca. English Lyric by Jon Hendricks.
Music by Antonio Carlos Jobim.

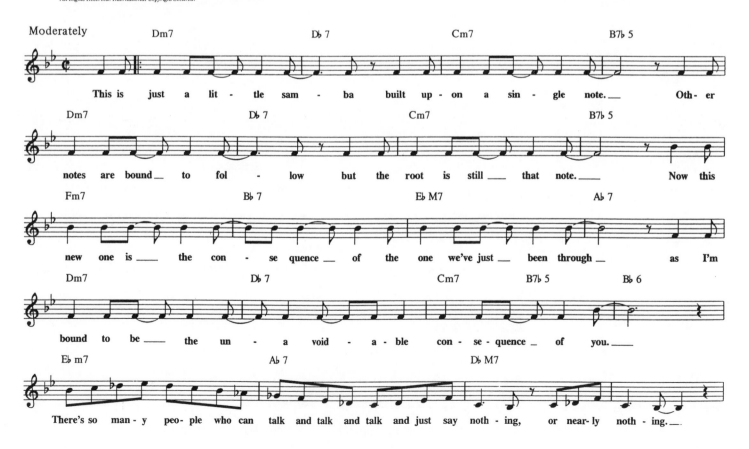

This is just a lit - tle sam - ba built up - on a sin - gle note. __ Oth - er

notes are bound __ to fol - low but the root is still __ that note. __ Now this

new one is __ the con - se quence __ of the one we've just __ been through __ as I'm

bound to be the un - a void - a - ble con - se - quence _ of you. __

There's so man - y peo - ple who can talk and talk and talk and just say noth - ing, or near - ly noth - ing. __

Db m7   Gb 7   Cb M7

I have used up all the scale I know and at the end I've come to noth - ing, or near - ly

Cm7b 5   B7b 5   Dm7   Db 7   Cm7   B7b 5

noth - ing. So I come back to ___ my first ___ note, as I must come back ___ to you. ___ I will

Dm7   Db 7   Cm7   B7b 5   Fm7

pour in - to ___ that one ___ note all the love I feel ___ for you. ___ An - y - one who wants ___ the whole ___

Bb 7   Eb M7   Ab 7   Db M7

___ show Re, Mi, Fa, Sol, La, ___ Ti Do, ___ he will find him - self with no ___

C7   Cb M7   1. Bb 6   F7#5   2. Bb 6

___ show. Bet - ter play ___ the note ___ you know. ___ This is ___

155. Passion Flower

By Billy Strayhorn.

© Copyright 1944 Tempo Music Incorporated, USA.
Campbell Connelly & Company Limited, 8/9 Frith Street, London W1.
All Rights Reserved. International Copyright Secured.

Moderately

F#9(b5)   F9(b5)   F#9(b5)   F9(b5)   E+9   Eb+9   D9   D7b9   G6/9   *Fine*   F#9(b5)

F9(b5)   F#9(b5)   F9(b5)   F#9(b5)   F9(b5)   E+9   Eb+9   D9   D7(b9)   G6/9

Dbmaj7   Cm7(b9)   B7(b5)   Bb7(b9)   A9(b5)   Ab7   Ab6   Db   Db6   Bb7(+11)   Eb7   Ab7(b5)   Db7

D.C. al Fine

156. Prezervation

By Stan Getz.

© Copyright 1969 Prestige Music Company Incorporated, USA.
Prestige Music Limited, 1 Wyndham Yard, Wyndham Place, London W1.
All Rights Reserved. International Copyright Secured.

Moderately

C7   Fm   Fm7   Dm7-5   Dbmaj7   D7

Gm   Eb   D7   Gm7   Fm7   Dm7-5

157. Petite Fleur (Little Flower)

Words & Music by Sidney Bechet.

158. The Pearls

By Ferdinand 'Jelly Roll' Morton.

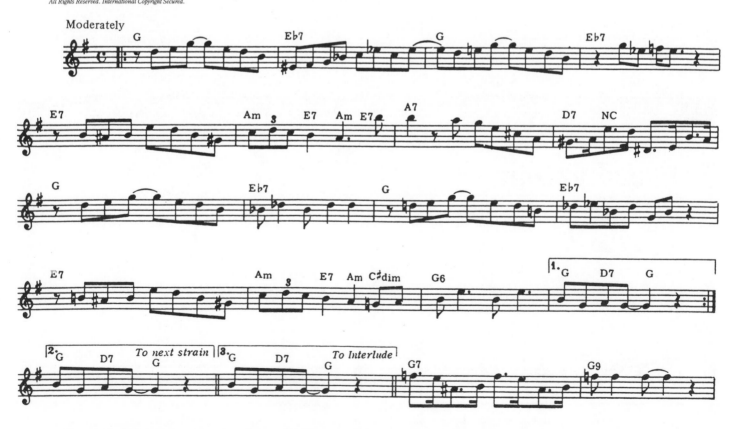

e Preacher

e Silver.

59 Silhouette Music Corporation, USA.
ic Limited, Suite 2.07, Plaza 535 Kings Road, London SW10 for the British Commonwealth (except Canada).
ed. International Copyright Secured.

160. Quiet Nights Of Quiet Stars

English Words by Gene Lees. Music & Original Words by Antonio Carlos Jobim.

© Copyright 1962, 1965 by Antonio Carlos Jobim, Brazil.
MCA Music Limited, 77 Fulham Palace Road, London W6 for the British Commonwealth (excluding Canada & South Africa).
All Rights Reserved. International Copyright Secured.

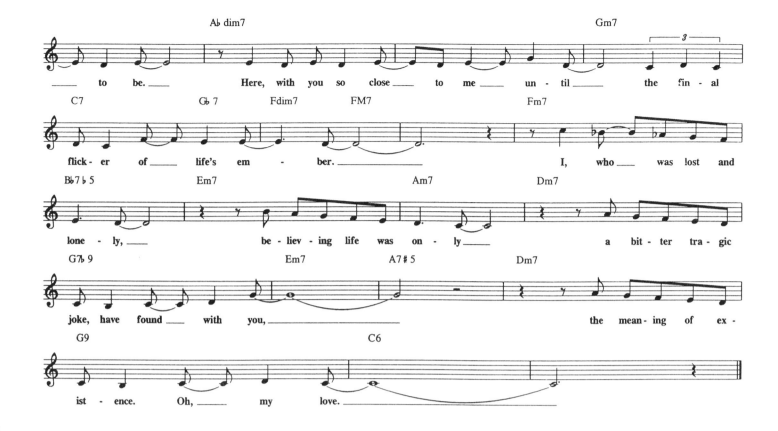

to be. Here, with you so close to me un - til the fin - al flick - er of life's em - ber. I, who was lost and lone - ly, be - liev - ing life was on - ly a bit - ter tra - gic joke, have found with you, the mean - ing of ex - ist - ence. Oh, my love.

161. Red Top

Words & Music by Lionel Hampton & Ken Kynard.

Medium Bounce

My lit - tle Red Top see how you got me spin - ning, go - ing 'round and 'round and I don't want to stop. You've got me so if I don't go a - round I'm sure gon - na drop, gon - na drop, gon - na drop, So Red Top you just go right on spin - ning, go 'round and 'round and don't you ev - er stop. Re - mem - ber, that if you don't go a - round we're sure gon - na drop, gon - na drop, gon - na drop.

162. Paul's Pal

By Sonny Rollins.

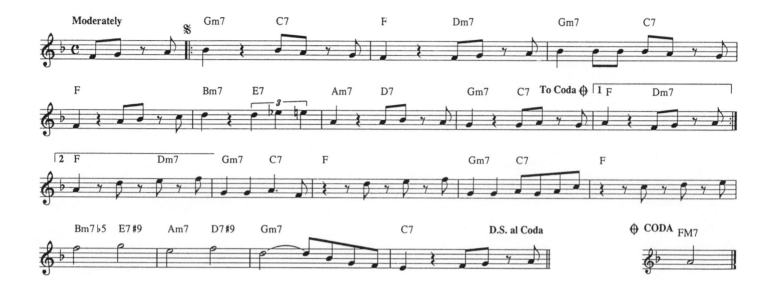

163. Quasimodo

By Charlie Parker.

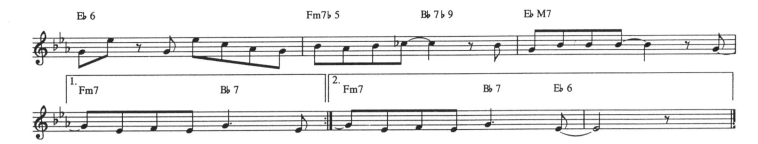

164. Ruby, My Dear

By Thelonious Monk.

Moderately

165. Red Beans

By Coleman Hawkins.

Medium Swing

D.C. and Fade

166. Raincheck

By Billy Strayhorn.

167. Riviera

By J.J. Johnson.

168. Roundhouse

By Gerry Mulligan.

169. Solitude

Words by Eddie de Lange & Irving Mills. Music by Duke Ellington.

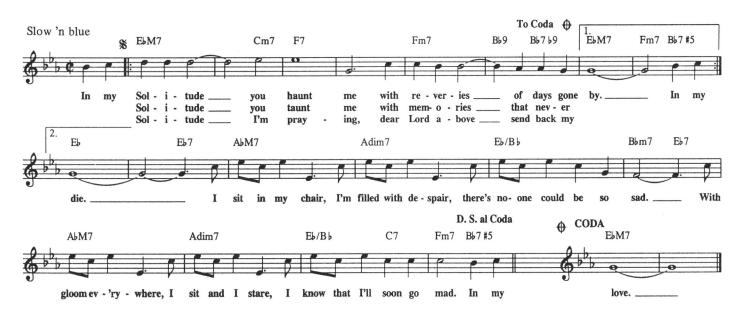

170. Someday (You'll Be Sorry)

Words & Music by Louis Armstrong.

171. Seven Eleven

By Carpenter & Williams.

172. Seven Come Eleven

By Benny Goodman & Charlie Christian.

Satin Doll

s by Johnny Mercer. Music by Duke Ellington & Billy Strayhorn.

Moderately

Cig - a - rette hold - er which wigs me, o - ver her shoul - der, she digs me.
Ba - by shall we___ go out skip - pin', care - ful a - mi - go, you're flip - pin'.

Out cat - tin' that Sat - in Doll.___
Speaks lat - in that Sat - in Doll.

She's no - bod - y's fool, so I'm play - ing it cool as can be.___

I'll give it a whirl, ___ but I ain't for no girl___ catch - ing me.___

(Spoken) Swich - E - Roo - ney Tel - e - phone num - bers well you know, do - ing my rhum - bas

with u - no, and that 'n' my Sat - in Doll.___

174. Salt Peanuts

Words & Music by John 'Dizzy' Gillespie & Kenny Clarke.

Moderately

175. Shawnuff

By Charlie Parker & John 'Dizzy' Gillespie.

176. Solar

By Miles Davis.

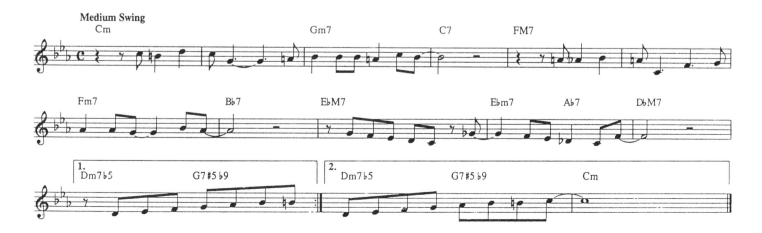

177. Say Listen

By Donald Byrd.

178. Straight Street

By John Coltrane.

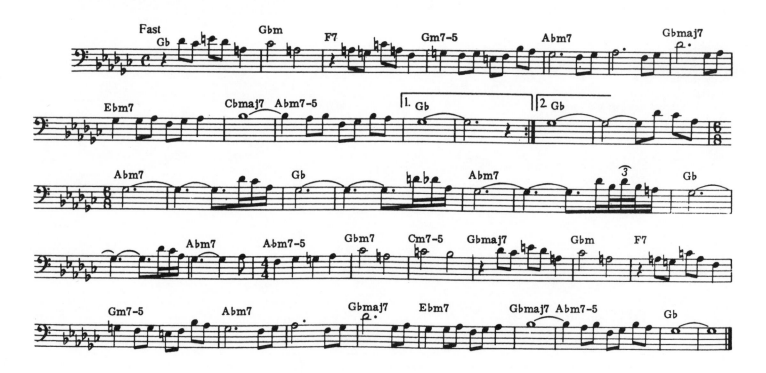

179. Slim Jim

By Donald Byrd.

180. Soul Searchin'

By Shirley Scott.

181. Short Stop

By Shorty Rogers.

182. Skin Deep

By Louis Bellson.

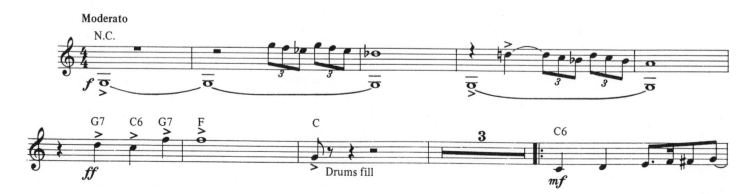

183. Sock

By Gene Ammons.

184. Spain

By Chick Corea.

185. Song Of The Jet (Samba Do Aviao)

Original Words & Music by Antonio Carlos Jobim. English Words by Gene Lees.

below ___ Dance the sam - ba as ___ they go, Shin - ing Ri - o, there ___ you lie, ___
es - ty ___ Climb - ing from a sil - ver sea, ___ Dark eyed girls ___ who smile ___ at me. ___

Cit - y of sun, of sea ___ and sky, Moun - tains of green ris - ing ___ so high. Four min - utes more, we'll be there
Cit - y of love and mys - ter - ies; Fas - ten seat belts, no smok - ing please. Now we're de - scend - ing and ev -

___ at the air - port of Ga - le - ão. ___ Ri - o de Ja - nei - ro, Ri - o de Ja - nei - ro,
'ry - thing's rush - ing And now the wheels ___

Ri - o de Ja - nei - ro, Ri - o de Ja - nei - ro. touch the ground. ___

186. St. Thomas

By Sonny Rollins.

Latin/Calypso

187. Solo Flight

By Benny Goodman, Charlie Christian & Jimmy Mundy.

Moderate jump tempo

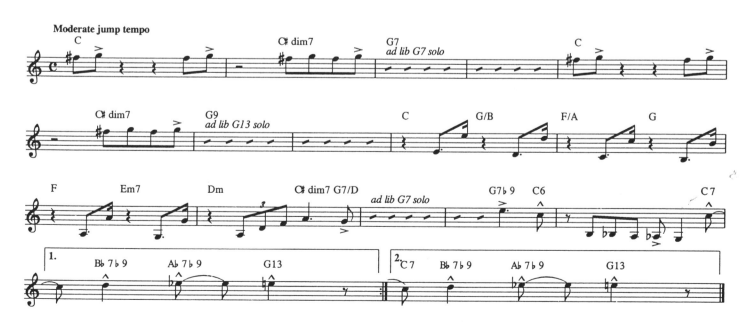

o Nice

Original Lyrics by Marcos Valle & Paulo Sergio Valle.
ics by Norman Gimbel.

Moderately

Some - one to hold me tight, that would be ver - y nice. Some - one to love me right that would be ver - y nice.

Some - one to un - der - stand each lit - tle dream in me. Some - one to take my hand, to be a team with me.

So Nice, life would be So Nice if one day I'd find some - one who would

take my hand and sam - ba thru life with me. Some - one to cling to me, stay with me right or wrong,

some - one to sing to me some lit - tle sam - ba song. Some - one to take my heart, then give his heart to me.

Some - one who's read - y to give love a start with me. Oh, yes, that would be So Nice.

Should it be you and me, I could see it would be nice. nice.

189. Struttin' With Some Barbecue

Words by Don Raye. Music by Louis Armstrong.

Moderately

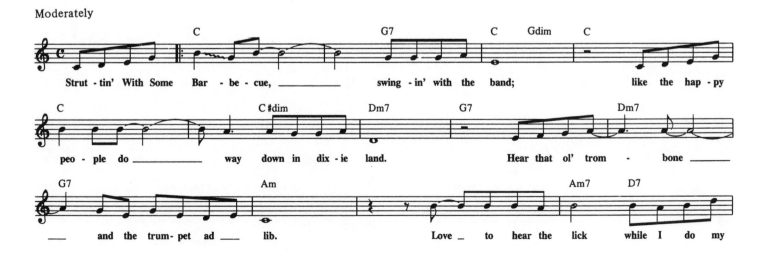

Strut - tin' With Some Bar - be - cue, swing - in' with the band; like the hap - py

peo - ple do way down in dix - ie land. Hear that ol' trom - bone

and the trum - pet ad lib. Love to hear the lick while I do my

pick - in', _____ pick - in' on a juic - y rib. 'Cause I'm Strut - tin' With Some Bar - be - cue, _____

_____ feel - in' might - y grand; pass an - oth - er help - in', please, _____ of that

good ol' _____ dix - ie land. _____ And mis - ter wait - er, _____ if you please, _____ an - oth - er

rib or two; _____ and I'll go strut, strut, stut - tin', Strut - tin' With Some Bar - be - cue _____

1. _____ Strut - tin' With Some _____

190. Stuffy

By Coleman Hawkins.

191. Shreveport Stomps

By Ferdinand 'Jelly Roll' Morton.

192. Strenuous Life

By Scott Joplin.

Not Too Fast

193. Stonewall

By Milt Jackson.

194. Solacium

195. Southside

196. So What

By Gerry Mulligan.

197. Swinging For Bumsy

By Sonny Rollins.

198. The Snow Is Green

By Yusef Lateef.

199. Soul Shouting

By Stanley Turrentine.

200. Some Stretching

By Coleman Hawkins.

201. Serene

By Eric Dolphy.

202. Sweetheart Of Sigmund Freud

By Shorty Rogers.

203. Soul Message

By Richard 'Groove' Holmes.

204. Soul Eyes

By Mal Waldron.

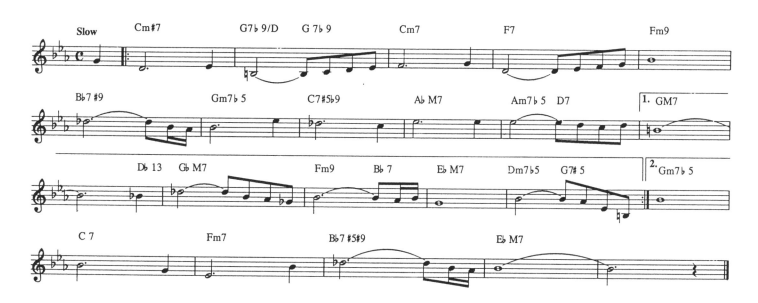

205. Squeeze Me

Words & Music by Clarence Williams & Thomas 'Fats' Waller.

206. Soul Junction

By Red Garland.

207. Splanky

By Neal Hefti.

xedo Junction

dy Feyne. Music by Erskine Hawkins, William Johnson & Julian Dash.
Music Publishing Company Incorporated, USA.
United Kingdom of Great Britain and Northern Ireland only by permission of Boosey &
imited.
ional Copyright Secured.

Medium Swing

Way down south, in Bir - ming - ham,_ I mean south in Al - a - bam's an old

place where peo - ple go _ to dance_ the night _ a - way._ They all drive or walk

_ for miles _ to get jive that south - ern style, s - low jive that makes_ you want _ to dance

_ 'til break_ of day. _ It's a junc - tion where the town folks meet.

At each func - tion, in their tux they_ greet_ you. Come on down, for - get

_ your care. _ Come on down. You'll find _ me there. So long town! I'm head - in' for _ Tux - e-

1. So long town! I'm head - in' for _ Tux - e-

2. Bb

- do Junc - tion now. _ Way down _

209. T'ain't What You Do
(It's The Way That Cha Do It)

Words & Music by Sy Oliver & James Young.

© Copyright 1939 MCA Music (a division of MCA Incorporated, USA).
MCA Music Limited, 77 Fulham Palace Road, London W6 for the world (excluding South and Central America, Japan,
Australasia and the Philippines).
All Rights Reserved. International Copyright Secured.

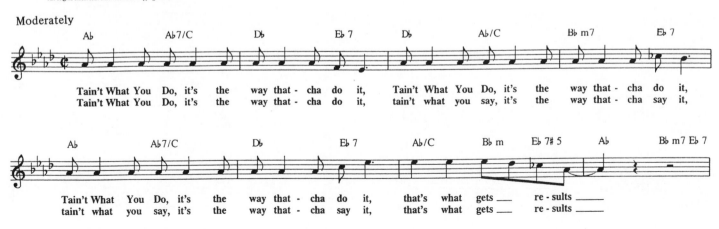

Moderately

Tain't What You Do, it's the way that - cha do it,   Tain't What You Do, it's the way that - cha do it,
Tain't What You Do, it's the way that - cha do it,   tain't what you say, it's the way that - cha say it,

Tain't What You Do, it's the way that - cha do it,   that's what gets _ re - sults _
tain't what you say, it's the way that - cha say it,   that's what gets _ re - sults

Tain't What You Do, it's the time that - cha do it, Tain't What You Do, it's the time that - cha do it,
tain't what you croon it's the way that - cha croon it, tain't what you croon it's the way that - cha croon it,

Tain't What You Do, it's the time that - cha do it, that's what gets ___ re - sults.___ You can
tain't what you croon it's the way that - cha croon it, that's what gets ___ re - sults.___ If you're

try hard___ don't mean a thing,___ take it ea - sy ___
lone - some ___ and on the shelf ___ it's your own fault,___

then your jive will swing.___ Tain't What You Do, it's the place that - cha do it,
so just blame your - self.___ Tain't what you sat, it's the place that - cha say it,

Tain't What You Do, it's the time that - cha do it, Tain't What You Do, it's the way that - cha do it,
tain't what you croon it's the time that - cha croon it, Tain't What You Do, it's the way that - cha do it,

that's what gets ___ re - sults.___
that's what gets ___ re - sults. ___

210. Time Remembered

By Bill Evans.

© Copyright 1965 Acorn Music Corporation, USA.
Kensington Music Limited, Suite 2.07, Plaza 535 Kings Road, London SW10.
All Rights Reserved. International Copyright Secured.

With Movement

211. The Toy Trumpet

Music by Raymond Scott. Words by Sidney D. Mitchell & Lew Pollack.

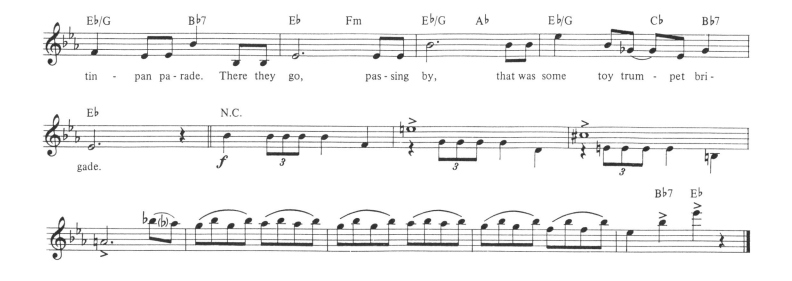

tin - pan pa - rade. There they go, pas - sing by, that was some toy trum - pet bri -

gade.

212. Take Five

By Paul Desmond.

213. Time's A-Wastin'

Words & Music by Duke Ellington, Mercer Ellington & Don George.

Lis - ten, ba-by, the TIME'S A-WAST - IN', ___ An' I'm tell-in' ya it's dis-grace - in'. ___

Miss-in' kiss-es we should be tast - in', ___ Sug-ar child, ___ now I'm beg-gin' your lips to has - ten. ___ I

need 'em so, ___ 'cause I got a feel-in' I got - ta glow. ___ While there's a moon up ___

can't our song be more than just a tune up? ___ Late-ly, dar-ling, I have learned a les - son, ___

More than just my dreams de - sire ca - ress-in'. ___ So, has-ten now ___ 'cause, ba - by, the time is a - wast - in' now. ___

214. Ting A Ling

By Louis Bellson & Charles Shavers.

215. Tuttie Flutie

By Herbie Mann.

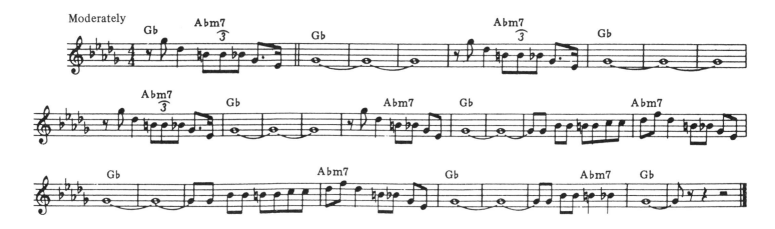

216. Three For Dizzy

By Roland Kirk.

217. Trane's Blues

By John Coltrane.

218. Ted Lewis Blues

By Ferdinand 'Jelly Roll' Morton.

219. That's A Plenty

Words by Ray Gilbert. Music by Lew Pollack.

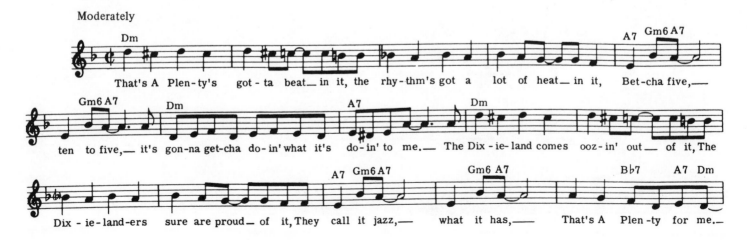

That's A Plen-ty's got-ta beat in it, the rhy-thm's got a lot of heat in it, Bet-cha five, ten to five, it's gon-na get-cha do-in' what it's do-in' to me. The Dix-ie-land comes ooz-in' out of it, The Dix-ie-land-ers sure are proud of it, They call it jazz, what it has, That's A Plen-ty for me.

220. Tenor Madness

By Sonny Rollins.
© *Copyright 1957 Prestige Music Company Incorporated, USA.*
Prestige Music Limited, 1 Wyndham Yard, Wyndham Place, London W1.
All Rights Reserved. International Copyright Secured.

Moderately

221. Tel Aviv

By Herbie Mann.

222. Tempus Fugit

By Earl Bud Powell.

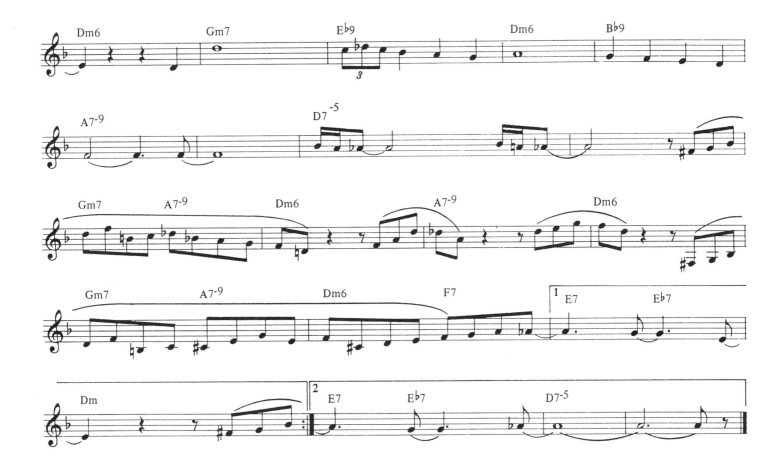

223. Tune Up

By Miles Davis.

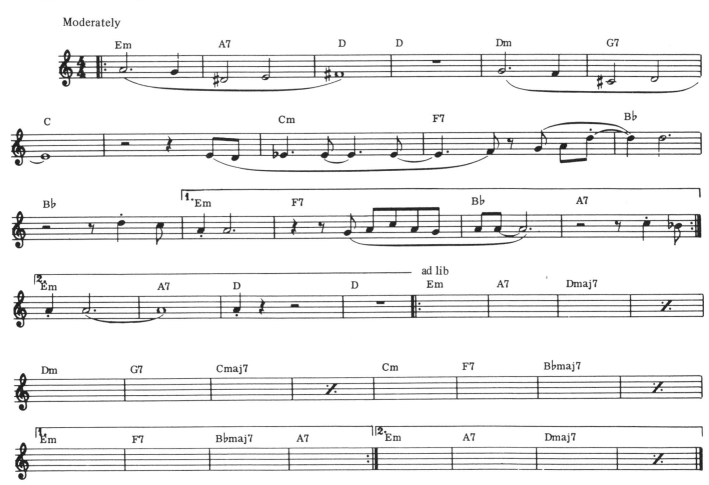

224. Tenor Conclave

By Hank Mobley.

© Copyright 1974 Prestige Music Company Incorporated, USA.
Prestige Music Limited, 1 Wyndham Yard, Wyndham Place, London W1.
All Rights Reserved. International Copyright Secured.

225. Twisted

By Annie Ross & Wardell Gray.

© Copyright 1965 Prestige Music Company Incorporated, USA.
Prestige Music Limited, 1 Wyndham Yard, Wyndham Place, London W1.
All Rights Reserved. International Copyright Secured.

ake The 'A' Train

& Music by Billy Strayhorn.
1941 Tempo Music Incorporated, USA.
elly & Company Limited, 8/9 Frith Street, London W1.
ved. International Copyright Secured.

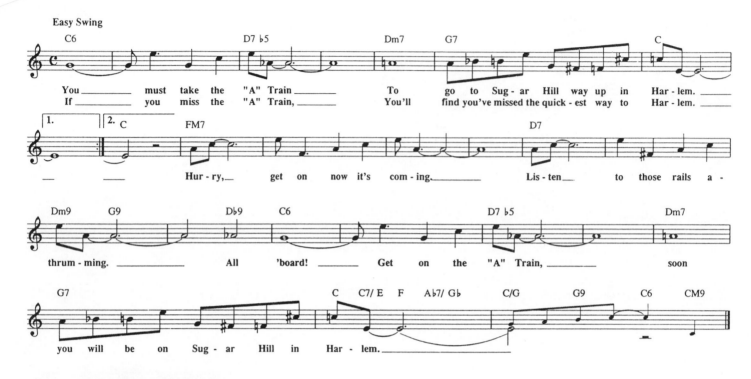

Easy Swing

You _____ must take the "A" Train _____ To go to Sug - ar Hill way up in Har - lem. _____
If _____ you miss the "A" Train, _____ You'll find you've missed the quick - est way to Har - lem. _____

— — Hur - ry, __ get on now it's com - ing. _____ Lis - ten __ to those rails a -

thrum - ming. _____ All 'board! __ Get on the "A" Train, _____ soon

you will be on Sug - ar Hill in Har - lem. _____

227. Undecided

Words by Sid Robin. Music by Charles Shavers.

© *Copyright 1939, 1954 by Leeds Music Corporation (Assigned to MCA Music, New York, USA).*
MCA Music Limited, 77 Fulham Palace Road, London W6 for the World (excluding North, Central and South America, Japan,
Australasia, and the Philippines).
All Rights Reserved. International Copyright Secured.

Moderately

First you say you do and then you don't, _____ and then you say you will and
Now you want to play, and then it's no, _____ and when you say you'll stay, that's
If you've got a heart and if your're kind, _____ then don't keep us a - part . Make

then you won't. __
when you go. _____ } You're Un - de - ci - ded now, so what are you go - na do? _____
up your mind. __

I've been sit - ting on a fence, and it does - n't make much sense, 'cause you

keep me in sus - pense and you know it. _____ Then you prom - ise to re - turn. When you

don't, I real - ly burn. Well, I guess I'll nev - er learn, and I show it. _____

228. That's Where It's At

By Shirley Scott.

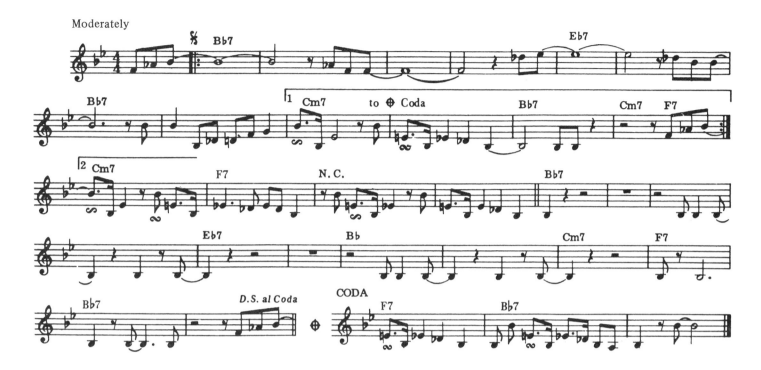

229. Traneing In

By John Coltrane.

230. Tubby

By Gene Ammons.

231. Valse Hot

By Sonny Rollins.

232. Waltz For Debby

Music by Bill Evans. Words by Gene Lees.

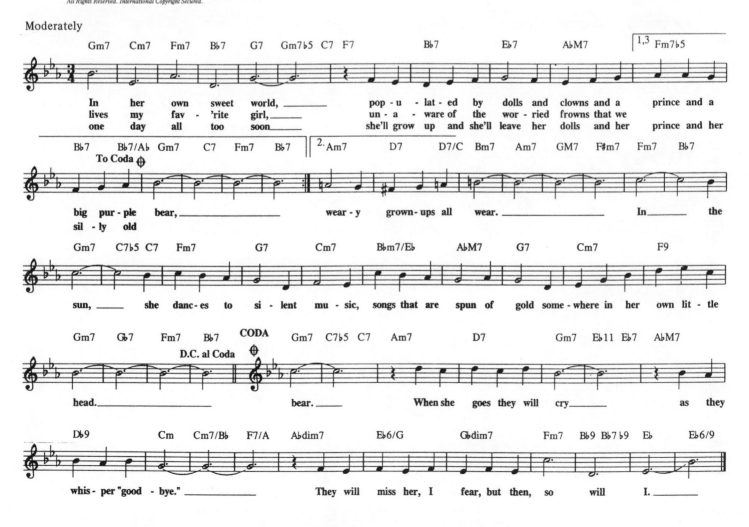

In her own sweet world, _____ pop - u - lat - ed by dolls and clowns and a prince and a
lives my fav - 'rite girl, _____ un - a - ware of the wor - ried frowns that we
one day all too soon_____ she'll grow up and she'll leave her dolls and her prince and her

big pur - ple bear, _____ wear - y grown-ups all wear. _____ In _____ the
sil - ly old

sun, _____ she danc - es to si - lent mu - sic, songs that are spun of gold some - where in her own lit - tle

head._____ bear. When she goes they will cry_____ as they

whis - per "good - bye." _____ They will miss her, I fear, but then, so will I. _____

233. Very Early

Music by Bill Evans. Words by Carol Hall.

Ver - y Ear - ly love came quick - ly when I first saw you. _____ You were all I
Ver - y Ear - ly I came run - ning like an ea - ger child; _____ love was all I

ev - er want - ed, strange how ear - ly I knew! _____ } Now the ear - ly rain beats on my
ev - er asked for love came won - drous and wild! _____ }

win - dow, sweet the sound rain can make. Nice to lie here, soft - ly sigh here, you and

I here wait - ing for the Ver - y Ear - ly _____ sun to wake. _____

234. Vierd Blues

By Miles Davis.

235. Walkin'

By Richard Carpenter.

236. Walkin' Shoes

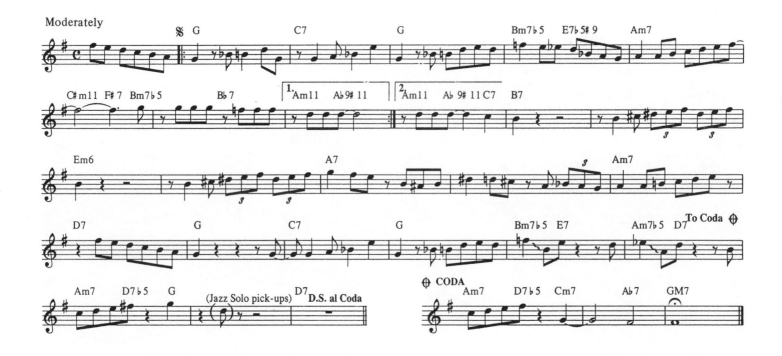

237. Winin' Boy Blues

won't you look at— Sis,— look at Sis.— Ma-ma, ma-ma, look at Sis;— out on the lev-ee do-in' the dou-ble twist.— I'm the win-in' boy,— Don't de-ny— my name.— I'm the win-in' boy,— (Hum) - - - - - - - - - - - - Oh Ba - by, Yes, I'm the win-in' boy,— Don't de - ny my name;— Pick it up and shake it like sweet Stav-in' Chain.—(Hum) - - - - - - - - - Don't de-ny— my— name.

238. Way Down Yonder In New Orleans

Words & Music by Henry Creamer & Turner Layton.

© Copyright 1922 by Shapiro Bernstein & Company Incorporated, USA.
Lawrence Wright Music Company Limited, 127 Charing Cross Road, London WC2.
All Rights Reserved. International Copyright Secured.

Moderately

'Way Down Yon - der In New-Or-leans — in the land — of dream-y scenes— there's a gar - den of E - den that's what I mean.— Cre-ole ba - bies with flash-ing eyes — soft - ly whis-per with ten - der sights — "Stop! Oh! won't you give your la - dy fair_____ a lit - tle smile," Stop! You bet your life you'll lin - ger there _____ a lit - tle while. There is Heav - en right here on earth__ with those beau - ti - ful / They've got an - gels right here on earth__ wear-ing lit - tle blue queens / jeans 'Way Down Yon - der In New Or - leans. leans.—

Waterworks

By Gerry Mulligan.

© Copyright 1969 Prestige Music Company Incorporated, USA.
Prestige Music Limited, 1 Wyndham Yard, Wyndham Place, London W1.
All Rights Reserved. International Copyright Secured.

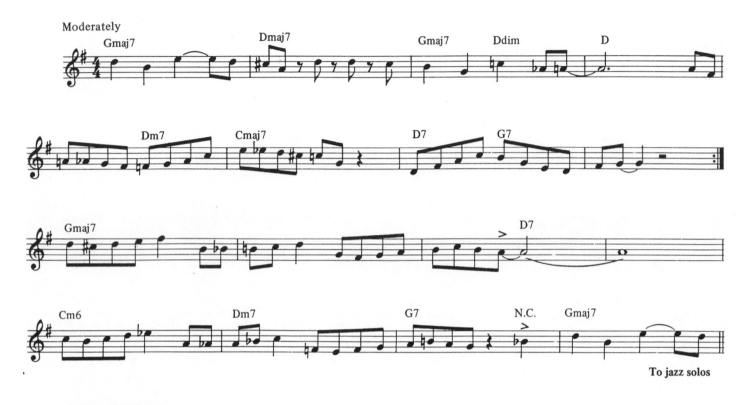

To jazz solos

240. Wooftie

By Chubby Jackson.

© Copyright 1953 Cromwell Music Incorporated, USA.
TRO Essex Music Limited, Suite 2.07, Plaza 535 Kings Road, London SW10.
All Rights Reserved. International Copyright Secured.

241. Wheatland (from the 'Canadiana Suite')

By Oscar Peterson.

242. Why Phillis

By Eugene Wright.

243. Wind Bag

By Kai Winding.

244. Will You Still Be Mine?

Words by Tom Adair. Music by Matt Dennis.

Moderately

When lov - ers make no ren - dez - vous _____ to stroll a - long Fifth Av - en - ue. _____
When glam - our girls have lost their charms, _____ when si - rens just mean false a - larms. _____

When this fa - mil - iar world is thru, _____ Will You Still Be Mine? _____
When lov - ers heed no call to

When cabs don't drive a - round the park, _____ no win - dows light the sum - mer dark. _____

When love has lost its sec - ret spark, _____. Will You Still Be Mine? _____ When moon-light

on the Hud - son's not ro - man-cy_____ and spring no lon - ger turns a young man's fan - cy.

CODA

arms, _____ Will You Still Be Mine? _____

245. Zootcase

By Zoot Sims.

Moderately

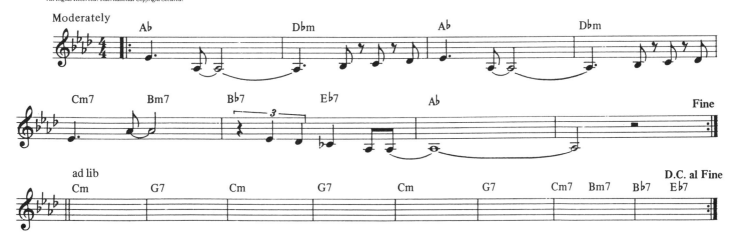

46. Yes Indeed (A Jive Spiritual)

Words & Music by Sy Oliver.

247. Walk Don't Run

By Shorty Rogers.

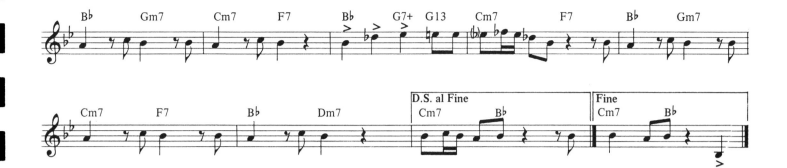

248. Zoot Swings The Blues

By Zoot Sims.

© Copyright 1964 Prestige Music Company Incorporated, USA.
Prestige Music Limited, 1 Wyndham Yard, Wyndham Place, London W1.
All Rights Reserved. International Copyright Secured.

249. Wholesale Dealin' Papa

By Brownie McGhee.

250. Weep No More

By Dave Brubeck.

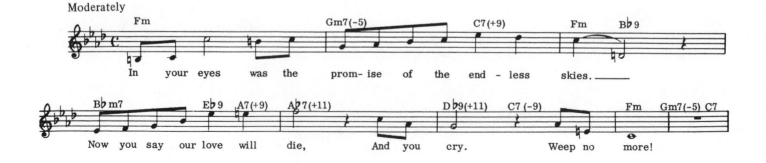

In your eyes was the prom- ise of the end- less skies. _____

Now you say our love will die, And you cry. Weep no more!

New from Music Sales - the one-and only, ultimate busker book! It's *the* book to take to a party... to a gig... on your holiday... or to that famous desert island!

It's packed with literally hundreds and hundreds of the best-loved songs of all time... from vintage standards of the 30s right through to the latest pop hits.

"The Suitcase Book"!

"Probably the best songbook in the world."

The Busker's Fake Book 1001 All-Time Hit Songs

"The only songbook you'll ever need!"

For piano, organ, guitar, all electronic keyboards and all 'C' instruments. With an easy-to-use A-Z title finder plus a classified 'song type' index. As a taster, here's just a quarter of the titles in this unique bumper songbook...

'A' You're Adorable
A Fine Romance
A Fool Such As I
A Hard Day's Night
A Man And A Woman
A Teenager In Love
Act Naturally
Against All Odds
Ain't Misbehavin'
All I Have To Do Is Dream
All My Loving
America
An American In Paris
An Old Fashioned Love Song
Angel Eyes
Another Suitcase In Another Hall
As Time Goes By
Band On The Run
Barbara Ann
Baubles Bangles And Beads
Because
Bennie And The Jets
Big Girls Don't Cry
Big Spender
Bird Dog
Blowin' In The Wind
Boogie Woogie Bugle Boy
Buffalo Gals
Bye Bye Love
California Dreaming
Can't Smile Without You
Candle In The Wind
Caravan
Chantilly Lace
Come Fly With Me
Consider Yourself
Crazy
Cruising Down The River
Dancing Queen
Daniel
Desafinado
Devil In Disguise
Diamonds Are A Girl's Best Friend
Do You Know The Way To San Jose
Don't Cry For Me Argentina
Don't Pay The Ferryman
Don't Sleep In The Subway
EastEnders
Ebony And Ivory
Eleanor Rigby
Empty Chairs At Empty Tables
The Entertainer
Every Breath You Take
First Time Ever I Saw Your Face
Fools Rush In
From Me To You
Funiculi, Funicula
Für Elise
Get Back
Get It On (Bang A Gong)
The Girl From Ipanema
Good Vibrations
Goodbye Yellow Brick Road
Guys And Dolls
Happy Xmas (War Is Over)
Havah Nagilah
He Ain't Heavy He's My Brother
Hello Mary Lou

Hello, Goodbye
Here, There And Everywhere
Hey Jude
Hey, Good Lookin'
Honeysuckle Rose
I Cangi I Saw I Conga'd
I Don't Want To Spoil The Party
I Dreamed A Dream
I Feel Pretty
I Fought The Law
I Left My Heart In San Francisco
I Saw Her Standing There
I'm A Loser
I'm Beginning To See The Light
I'm Still Standing
If I Had A Hammer
If I Were A Bell
In The Air Tonight
It Never Rains In Southern California
It's Not Unusual
It's So Easy
Jambalaya
Jealous Guy
La Roade De l'Amour
Lady D'Arbanville
The Lady In Red
The Lambeth Walk
The Last Time I Saw Paris
Layla
Leaning On A Lamp Post
Let It Be
Let's Twist Again
The Lion Sleeps Tonight
Live And Let Die
Long Tall Sally
Love And Marriage
Lover Man
Lucille
Luck Be A Lady
Lullaby Of Birdland
Maple Leaf Rag
Maria
Me And My Girl
Mister Bojangles
Money For Nothing
Mull Of Kintyre
Never On A Sunday
Nights In White Satin
Norwegian Wood
Not Fade Away
O Sole Mio
Oh Pretty Woman
Ol' Man River
Old Shep
On A Slow Boat To China
Only The Lonely
P.S. I Love You
Peggy Sue
Pennies From Heaven
Penny Lane
Pigalle
Poison Ivy
The Power Of Love
Raindrops Keep Falling On My Head
Rave On
Rhapsody In Blue
Riders On The Storm
Rock Around The Clock

Ruby Don't Take Your Love To Town
Satin Doll
Scarborough Fair
Shake Rattle And Roll
She Loves You
Singing The Blues
Sixteen Tons
Sloop John B
Smoke Gets In Your Eyes
Solitude
Something
Somewhere
Spanish Eyes
Standing On The Corner
Stars Fell On Alabama
Stranger In Paradise
Strangers In The Night
Streets Of London
Sugarbush
Sultans Of Swing
Summertime Blues
Sunshine Of Your Love
Sweet Charity
Swing Low, Sweet Chariot
Take Back Your Mink
Take That Look Off Your Face
Take The 'A' Train
Teen Angel
The Tender Trap
That'll Be The Day
Theme For A Dream
These Foolish Things
They Didn't Believe Me
This Guy's In Love With You
This Land Is Your Land
Those Were The Days
Three Little Fishies
Till There Was You
To Know Him Is To Love Him
Tonight
True Love Ways
Tulips From Amsterdam
Tutti Frutti
Unchained Melody
Under The Boardwalk
Up, Up And Away
Uptown Girl
The Very Thought Of You
Wake Up Little Susie
Walk Tall
The Way You Look Tonight
We Can Work It Out
We Don't Need Another Hero
We Shall Overcome
We'll Meet Again
What Kind Of Fool Am I
Wheels
When I'm Sixty Four
When Irish Eyes Are Smiling
When This Lousy War Is Over
Where Have All The Flowers Gone
Witchcraft
With A Little Help From My Friends
Woman
Yellow Submarine
Yesterday
Your Cheatin' Heart
Your Song

Melody, lyrics and guitar chords to literally hundreds and hundreds of the best songs of all time... from the golden standards through to the great pop hits of today.

Wise Publications
Order No. AM94947

While compiling this huge book, editor/arranger Peter Lavender kept all the artwork in a huge suitcase! But now that it's printed, this new mega-bumper busker book is a lot easier to carry around!

Surprisingly portable, in fact, at the usual songbook size of 12" x 9"... with some 656 pages!

As well as the 1,001 songs, the book includes a handy A-Z alphabetical title index *and* a classified index, too.